JUST
· DRAW ·
ONE THING
· TODAY ·

METRO BOOKS
New York

An Imprint of Sterling Publishing Co., Inc.
1166 Avenue of the Americas
New York, NY 10036

ISBN 978-1-4351-6558-8

For information about custom editions, special sales, and premium and corporate
purchases, please contact Sterling Special Sales at 800-805-5489
or specialsales@sterlingpublishing.com.

Manufactured in China

2 4 6 8 10 9 7 5 3 1

www.sterlingpublishing.com

MIX
Paper from
responsible sources
FSC® C016973

JUST
· DRAW ·
ONE THING
· TODAY ·

*365 Creative Prompts
to Inspire You Every Day*

John Gillard

METRO BOOKS
New York

HOW THE BOOK WORKS

Each page of the book is color coded with one of four different color tabs. This indicates the type of prompt for each day.

SINGLE-PAGE PROMPTS

Developing fundamental skills, such as use of tone, texture, techniques, perspective, use of light and shade; often encouraging experimentation and sometimes playful.

FIRST HALF-PAGE PROMPTS

Developing key observational and drawing skills. These will often encourage creating compositions for a still life, or drawing studies in close-up detail.

SECOND HALF-PAGE PROMPTS

Promoting the same key elements of drawing as the first half-page prompts; often following the previous day's prompt.

INTENSIVE WEEK

More intensive drawing exercises, which require your own sketchpad in order to create larger pieces of work. Intensive week encourages you to experiment, develop, and hone your skills; often drawing inspiration from the great artists of the past.

INTRODUCTION

Just Draw One Thing Today offers inspiration and prompts to help you draw every day. Whether you work in a creative industry and want to get your creative juices flowing; have been drawing all your life; or simply enjoyed drawing as a child and want to relive sitting with pencil and paper, letting your imagination take you away, this book is for you.

Many of the prompts will require you to source an image, view a subject in front of you, or use your memory and imagination. You should feel free to use the prompts in whatever way suits you. For inspiration and reference, you may want to use books, the Internet, or photographs. You could use these to draw photo-realistic copies, or for creating your own interpretations of an object, place, or person. Some days you might draw from life.

A mixture of media can be used for drawing: try pencil, ballpoint pen, charcoal, pastel, or felt-tip marker. This book will focus on pencil drawing, although you should feel free to interpret the prompts however you wish. Creativity is all about freedom, and that is the primary purpose of this book.

Daily drawing gives life to creative ideas, and helps us observe and interpret what we see around us. Over time—a week, a month, a year—a new and unique style may emerge, one that has been waiting to be tapped into. Daily drawing may lead to larger projects, perhaps aiding other artistic disciplines, such as painting, printing, and collage. Developing your drawing skills can help you plan artistic projects, as you allow ideas to evolve freely. Drawing can give structure to larger pieces of art. Who knows where daily drawing may lead: a book full of your original sketches, inspiration for further creativity, an exhibition of your work, or simply the pleasure and creative release that comes from drawing each and every day.

1

HAT

Draw a hat. This could be an observation drawing from life, a photograph, or perhaps a famous hat from history, such as Abraham Lincoln's top hat.

2

LETTERING

Using ornate lettering, draw your name or initials.

SHADING SHAPES

Use the space below to sketch a series of simple shapes and fill them in using a few different methods of shading. These might be:

- hatch (a series of perpendicular lines)
- crosshatch (hatch lines crossing each other vertically and horizontally)
- shading (blending darker tones into lighter tones)
- tight circles (small circles drawn close together)
- stipple (a series of dots)
- random scribbles

GRAPHITE SCALE

The hardness of a pencil lead is measured on a graphite grading scale, from 9H to 9B. The harder the lead the lighter the pencil mark. The softer the lead the darker and more textured the mark. Draw four simple shapes and shade each of them from light to dark using four varying grades of pencil; perhaps 2H, 2B, 4B, and 8B.

5

DOODLE

Doodle across this entire page—any way you'd like. Be as chaotic as you want to be! Give your pencil complete freedom: doodle around the quote below, the blue tab at the top of the page, doodle in and around the word "doodle."

"The doodle is the brooding of the hand."
—Saul Steinberg

SMOOTH SHADING

Find an object which is both smooth and reflects light, such as a ceramic coffee mug. Draw the object and shade it in to add depth to your drawing. Use your finger to rub the pencil marks, making them smooth to convey the texture of the object. Use an eraser to pick out the flecks of light reflected on the object.

VANISHING POINT: TREES

Using the guidelines below, draw a line of trees leading to a vanishing point on the right. The trees should reduce in size the closer they get to the vanishing point.

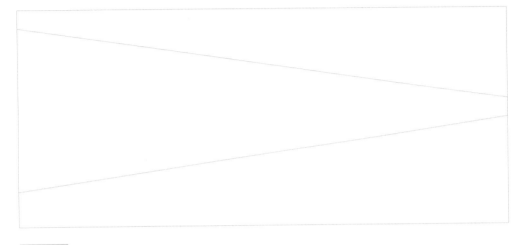

A WATERY LANDSCAPE

Draw a landscape which includes a water element, such as a lake, a river, or the sea.

INTENSIVE WEEK

Get your sketchpad and prepare to draw five larger pieces.

9

M. C. ESCHER: Escher drew optical illusions, such as a series of connected stairs that appear to all move in an upward direction. In one such illusion, he drew two hands drawing each other. Taking inspiration from Escher, draw your hand drawing your hand.

10

SELF-PORTRAIT: Draw a self-portrait that expresses a particular emotion, such as anger, happiness, or sorrow.

11

OLD BOOTS: Draw a pair of old boots. Try to get the oldest, most dilapidated pair you can. Has age brought a sense of character to these old boots? If you don't have any, use a photograph or your memory to complete this drawing.

12

IMAGINED CHARACTER: Draw an imagined character who might frequent one of the following establishments: a pool hall, a casino, a Turkish bath, a wine bar. You may want to use researched photographs, your imagination, or visit the location.

13

SHADOW PUPPET THEATER: Draw a scene in the style of a shadow puppet theater, where all the actions and emotions are conveyed through the use of silhouettes.

"Inspiration exists, but it has to find you working."

—Pablo Picasso

14 CLOTHING

Compose a still life of an item of clothing. It could be folded neatly or scattered haphazardly, hanging from a clothes hanger or line. Make an observation drawing, capturing the textures, folds, and any unique features; for example: rips, broken zippers, and chunky buttons.

15 POLAR BEAR

Draw a polar bear set against a snowy white background, using subtle shading to distinguish the bear from its surroundings.

16 PANDA

Use a photograph or your memory to draw a panda using two tones: a dark tone to build up the image of the black-and-white panda, and a second tone to pencil in a background, which in turn will complete the form of the panda.

17 CLOUDS

Look into the sky and draw any clouds you can see. If there are no clouds, draw from memory.

18 KING OF HERBS

Botanical drawing has a long tradition. The plant kingdom was once cataloged by scientists using detailed sketches. Draw a basil plant, known as the "king of herbs." Draw either from your imagination, from an image, or if you can purchase some basil draw it from life (you can always use it afterward in your cooking!).

19 COMPOSITION

Place three or four objects on a table and experiment with how best to arrange them. Use the thumbnails below to roughly sketch out potential compositions for a more detailed drawing tomorrow.

20 OBJECTS ON A TABLE

Choose your preferred composition from yesterday and use the space below to draw it in greater detail.

21 DRAW WHAT YOU FEEL

The English artist and sculptor Barbara Hepworth famously said, "I rarely draw what I see. I draw what I feel in my body." Draw something, real or abstract, which represents what you feel inside at this moment.

22 READING

Draw a very loose and gestural sketch of somebody reading a book.

23 LOW-LEVEL LIGHT SOURCE

Sit in a darkened room and shine a lamp or flashlight from a low level up toward your face. Sketch how your face appears in this light, drawing only those areas of dark shadow.

INTENSIVE WEEK

Get your sketchpad and prepare to draw five larger pieces.

24

VINCENT VAN GOGH: Van Gogh drew in a loose yet structured and considered style. He used small chaotic lines with varying degrees of weight to build up tone, form, and perspective. He worked mostly in Provence, France, often sketching pastoral scenes of farm workers at harvest, hay stacks, wheat fields, farm houses, and cypress trees. Taking inspiration from the drawing style of Van Gogh, draw a rural harvest landscape.

25

BEDROOM: Van Gogh painted pictures of his room in the Yellow House in Arles, France. Draw your own bedroom, again using the hatch-stroke style of Van Gogh.

26

SUNFLOWERS: Between 1887 and 1889 Van Gogh produced a series of paintings depicting sunflowers in a vase; some in full bloom, some wilting. Draw some flowers in a vase, either from your imagination, real life, or a sourced image. You could produce your own interpretation of Van Gogh's *Sunflowers* (1888).

27

REDRAW: Many artists produce a whole series of works on the same subject. Return to the first drawing you made this week and redraw it. Consider how you could make the new drawing an improvement on the last one, perhaps by modifying your technique or the composition.

28

STILL LIFE: Set up a still life. Use some of the techniques and style you have developed over the last few days.

"In spite of everything I shall rise again: I will take up my pencil, which I have forsaken in my great discouragement, and I will go on with my drawing."

—Vincent van Gogh

29 SNOWY MOUNTAIN

Draw a snow-topped mountain. Use your imagination, a book, or a photograph for reference. Alternatively, if you happen to be in view of a mountain, draw from life. Consider starting out with a darker tone for the winter sky, and then using the negative space to create the form of the snowy mountain.

30 ROCKY MOUNTAIN

Draw the same mountain as yesterday after the snow has melted away, and the rocks and plant life are uncovered. Consider how the tones of mountain and sky will be altered.

LIGHT SOURCE: CASTING SHADOWS

Choose an object which is not overly complex in shape or decoration—perhaps a vase—and place it on a table so that light from a window or lamp is shining on one side. Sit where you can observe the effect of the light upon the object. Does the placement of the object cause the light to cast a shadow on the table? What effect does the light have on the edges of the object?

LIGHT SOURCE: CHANGING VIEWPOINT

Using the same setup as yesterday, with the same object and light source, change your sitting position so you are drawing from a different viewpoint.

AIRPLANE WINDOW

Imagine you are in an airplane at 30,000 feet. Draw what you might see from the window, whether it be clouds, a city, arable land, lakes, rivers, or something else. If you are on a plane today then draw what you can actually see.

34 SHADOW

Draw a small pig in the left-hand corner of the space below, imagining the low light source of a setting sun. Using the rest of the space draw the relatively large and elongated shadow that would be cast by the pig.

35 EDGE OF A FOREST

Draw a row of trees growing tightly together on the edge of a forest.

INTENSIVE WEEK

Get your sketchpad and prepare to draw five larger pieces.

36   **DOORWAY:** Draw a door that is closed or partly open. Start by drawing areas of dark tone from which negative space will emerge. Begin to build up the image further by adding in lighter tones. Observe the areas of light and dark tone within an elaborate architrave, or the darkness behind a half-opened door.

37   **SKATEBOARDER:** Draw a skateboarder.

38   **CREST:** Draw a crest for you or your family incorporating one or two elements which represent your subject. You may want to base your design on an existing crest, such as a royal coat of arms or your favorite sports team.

39   **A FAMOUS DRAWING:** Source an image of a famous drawing and copy it as closely as possible in order to learn from the techniques of the artist.

40   **DRAWING FROM LITERATURE:** Use one or all of the following book titles as inspiration for a drawing:
- *Brave New World* by Aldous Huxley
- *Arctic Dreams* by Barry Lopez
- *On the Road* by Jack Kerouac

"Do not fail, as you go on, to draw something every day, for no matter how little it is, it will be well worth while, and it will do you a world of good."
—Cennino Cennini

41   FIVE-MINUTE SKETCH: ROLLING HILLS

Drawing with speed, completing your picture within five minutes, draw a landscape of rolling hills in the countryside and anything else you want to include, such as a small village.

42   REARVIEW MIRROR

Imagine you are in the front seat of a car. Draw what you might see when you look into the rearview mirror.

SLENDER FIGURE

Use a loose sketching style to draw a front and reverse view of a tall and slender figure.

Front view

Reverse view

44 VACATION

Draw the name of a well-known vacation destination. Use hand-drawn lettering and decoration that represents the character of the place.

45 A GATE

Draw a fence or gate and its surrounding environment. This might be the ornate gate of a large house, a garden fence, or a rural wire fence.

TEN-MINUTE SKETCH: GYMNAST

Drawing with speed, completing your picture within ten minutes, draw a gymnast performing a movement, such as a somersault. Draw the sequence in three or more stages. Make fast, flowing marks; chaotic lines that will add to the feeling of movement.

TEN-MINUTE SKETCH: MERGING MOVEMENT

Drawing with speed, continue onto this page the movement of yesterday's gymnast, so that the two drawings merge across the two pages. Imagine what the gymnast's next movement might be; perhaps a mid-air leg split.

RANDOM SPACE

Use the line below as part of a composition. The line could be an integral part of your drawing, or a dividing line between two separate drawings.

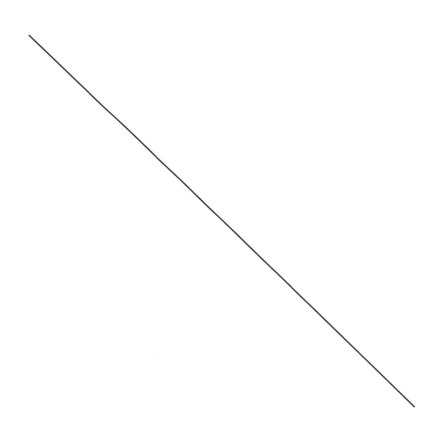

49 LOVE

Use the space below to create a single small drawing that conveys the idea of love.

50 HATE

Use the space below to create a single small drawing that conveys the idea of hate.

INTENSIVE WEEK

Get your sketchpad and prepare to draw five larger pieces.

51

BUILDING TONE: Place a white object in front of you; for example: a cup, a piece of scrunched up paper, a t-shirt, or an ornament. Begin by shading in the darker tones that surround the object. The shape of the white object will begin to form. Once the object has emerged, pencil in all the mid-tones on the object where shadows have been cast from, for example, the folds of a t-shirt, or the handle of a cup. Pencil in all of the light tones, such as where an ornament reflects the light. The object will leap from the page.

52

AN ICONIC SCENE: Draw an iconic moment from a film. A good example might be the scene from *Shawshank Redemption* in which Andy Dufresne, having finally escaped prison, falls to his knees and lifts his hands to the thunderous sky. You could copy a still of your chosen film, watch the scene, or draw from memory.

53

TIME CAPSULE, 1897: A time capsule has been found following the digging up of ground in a public park. It is discovered that the capsule was buried in 1897. Draw the scene of its uncovering, the contents of the capsule, or the scene of its original burial.

54

ART NOUVEAU: Using an Art Nouveau style, draw a portrait of a woman.

55

RELAXING: Draw somebody relaxing in a chair, sofa, or on a bed; at home, in a coffee shop, on a train, or somewhere else.

"With lead he shaded love into the woman's eyes."

—Dean Koontz

56 SOFT TO THE TOUCH

Choose something to draw that is soft to touch. Aim to convey the softness through delicate shading and subtle tone by using light and mid-tones rather than the harsher, heavy contrast of light and dark. You could also use your finger to rub the marks of pencil, creating a smooth texture.

57 AN OLD WATCH

Draw an old watch. You could, if you own one, draw the watch from real life, or refer to a sourced image. Alternatively, imagine a watch covered in cobwebs, found in a box in the attic.

HOME

Draw a room in your home. Try to observe and capture details you may often overlook, such as discoloration on an aging armchair, or reflections on the surface of a varnished table.

59 ROOM DETAIL

Choose a section—small, medium, or large—from your drawing on the previous page. Use the square frame below to draw this section in greater detail.

"Drawing makes you see things clearer, and clearer and clearer still, until your eyes ache."

—David Hockney

STATUE

Draw a statue. Use a sourced image or work from life, memory, or your imagination. What is the effect of the light source on the figure's form? How can it be distinguished from a real-life figure?

61   JEWELRY

Draw some jewelry. Observe the curves and angles and consider how you might interpret these using the strokes of your pencil.

62   SHOES

Using a photo-realist style, draw a pair of shoes, capturing all the tiny details which give them unique character.

SONG INSPIRATION

Use one or all of the following song titles as inspiration for a drawing:

- "House of the Rising Sun" (The Animals)
- "Ode to the Little Brown Shack Out Back" (Billy Edd Wheeler)
- "Rocking Chair in Hawaii" (George Harrison)

64   OBJECTS IN THE CLOSET

Look inside a closet to find an object, and then sketch it.

INTENSIVE WEEK

Get your sketchpad and prepare to draw five larger pieces.

65   **A BOXER**: Draw a boxer. You could look at grainy, historical photographs of famous boxers like Jack Dempsey, or pictures of boxers from more modern times, such as Roy Jones Jr. You may want to draw an iconic image, such as Mohammed Ali standing over Sonny Liston after his knockout punch. You may even know a boxer who will sit for you so you can draw from life.

66   **MAN WITH FACIAL HAIR**: Draw a portrait of a man with a mustache or beard, including either his entire figure or just the face. If you wish, choose a context in which to place your subject.

67   **KITCHEN CUPBOARD**: Draw an open kitchen cupboard, including its contents.

68   **STAINED GLASS**: Draw a stained glass window or create your own design for one. Be sure to include the clear and bold edges formed by the interconnecting lead framework.

69   **BALANCE**: Balance two or three objects on top of one another. Observe carefully the dimensions of each object, and their points of balance. Any inaccuracies in your drawing will make the objects look unnaturally balanced.

"We who draw do so not only to make something visible to others, but also to accompany something invisible to its incalculable destination."

—John Berger

70

NEWSPAPER

Draw a newspaper (or newspapers) folded up and placed on a table.

71

INSPIRATION FROM THE 50s

Draw something from the 1950s, for example: your grandmother's yearbook photo, a Chevy pickup truck, or an antique tin.

VANISHING POINT

The guidelines below give a starting point for drawing a scene in which the foreground is vanishing into a distant point on the horizon. Use these guidelines as a structure for your own scene. The central triangular guideline could be a path, a road, or a river. Anything which appears along the "path" will get gradually smaller the closer it gets to the vanishing point, as indicated by the fainter, converging perspective guidelines to the right and left of the path and horizon lines.

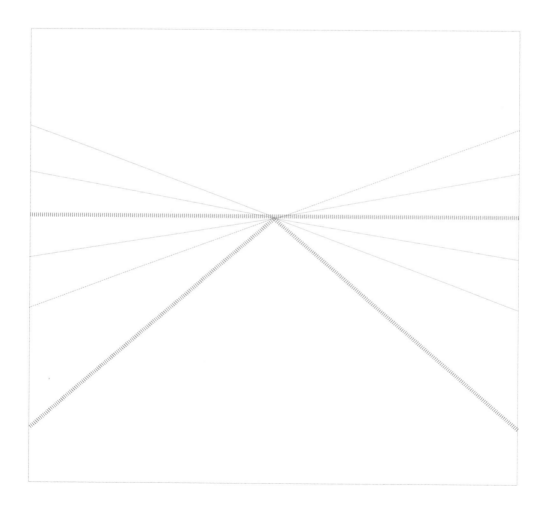

73 FIVE-MINUTE SKETCH: BULL

Draw a bull in just five minutes. Let your pencil fly across the page to make interpretative marks that create the idea and essence of the animal. A likeness is less important than fluidity.

74 TIGER

Draw a tiger. This could be a photo-realist drawing using a sourced image, or a more abstract interpretation from your imagination.

75 GIRAFFE

Draw a giraffe eating leaves from a tree.

76 A BAG

Draw a bag, whether it be an old leather suitcase with lots of cracks and character, a crumpled paper bag, or a new pristine handbag.

77 A CIRCLE INTO A SPHERE

Firstly, shade in the circle below to make it a sphere. Secondly, using only shading and no outline, draw a sphere in the empty space to the right of the circle.

INTENSIVE WEEK

Get your sketchpad and prepare to draw five larger pieces.

78 **HEAVY RAINFALL:** Draw an urban scene in heavy rainfall. You may want to use fast angular strokes with the pencil to mirror the force of the rainfall, and softer marks to mirror the lighter splashes as the rain bounces from the road and sidewalk.

79 **CEREMONIAL CLOTHING:** Draw a figure wearing ceremonial clothing.

80 **GHOST TOWN:** Draw a run-down wooden lodge in a Gold Rush ghost town.

81 **ZEBRA:** Zebras are another one of those animals, like pandas, penguins, racoons, and polar bears—among others—whose coloring lends them perfectly to the art of building negative shapes from darker tones. With this in mind, draw a zebra.

82 **NFL LOGOS:** Choose an NFL football team logo and draw a realistic representation of the logo's icon. For the New England Patriots, for example, draw a soldier who fought for American Independence, or for the Los Angeles Rams, sketch a realistic ram.

"Originality depends only on the character of the drawing and the vision peculiar to each artist."

—Georges Seurat

83 A BENCH

Draw a scene which includes a bench. It could be an urban or rural setting, or somewhere else, such as a seafront.

84 CREATURES OF THE OCEAN

Draw a shark, dolphin, or whale swimming in the ocean.

SATIRE

Caricatures are often used as instruments of satire. One way in which to produce a caricature is to draw as close a likeness as possible, while accentuating one or two prominent features and attaching the head to a small body. Draw a caricature of yourself or somebody else. You may also want to set your caricature in a suitable context.

FLAME

Draw a flame emanating from an open fire, a lighter, a candle, or something else.

A PATCHWORK QUILT

Draw a patchwork quilt on a bed, either the entire quilt or just a study of a section; perhaps observing how it drapes over the edge of the bed. Draw as much or as little detail as you like, but aim to depict the distortion of the patchwork fabric as it creases and drapes.

88 RANDOM SCRIBBLES

Draw a wild, random scribble in the space below and then try to create something from it. A scribble might end up as an elephant on roller-skates or a woman blowing a kiss.

89 OLD-FASHIONED TELEPHONE

Draw an old-fashioned telephone, either from life (if you have one) or from a sourced image.

GLOVE

Make a blind contour drawing of your hand in a glove. As you draw, avoid taking your pencil from the page or your eyes from the glove.

91 HEADDRESS

Draw a Native American feathered war bonnet, either being worn or set aside on an empty surface.

92 BICYCLE

Draw a bicycle, either stationary or being ridden. If it is stationary then focus on the textures and angles of the moving parts. If it is being ridden, focus on capturing the essence of movement.

INTENSIVE WEEK

Get your sketchpad and prepare to draw five larger pieces.

93   **TIME CAPSULE, 1963:** A time capsule has been found following the digging up of ground at the end of a garden. It is discovered that the capsule was buried in 1963. Draw the scene of its uncovering, the contents of the capsule, or the scene of its original burial.

94   **YOUR HOME:** Draw the exterior of the building you live in.

95   **GLASSES:** Draw a person wearing glasses. You may want to place them within a context or just focus on the figure. Consider the difference in tone between the lenses in the frames and the person's skin, and any distortion to the eyes the glasses may have created.

96   **RUN-DOWN MOTEL:** Draw the outside of an old run-down motel, aging mansion, or dilapidated bar. Use the strokes of your pencil to really get the feel of decay and age.

97   **CARNIVAL:** Draw a street carnival scene. You might imagine the scene from a distance, offering an impression of a huge crowd and vibrant movement, or close-up, in among the crowds and procession, capturing all the detail.

"All art is but dirtying the paper delicately."
—John Ruskin

98 TOYS AND GAMES

Draw a toy, such as a doll or teddy bear, or a game, such as dice or checkers.

99 PEN

Using a photo-realist style, draw a pen that has text or branding on its side. Drawing text on a curved surface requires careful observation and a delicate use of the pencil.

ICEBERG

Draw an iceberg showing both the tip above the surface of the water and the greater mass below. The tip accounts for only a small proportion of an iceberg's overall size. Consider also how you might convey the visual effect of the water on the submerged section.

101 FRUIT BOWL

Draw that classic still life that so many great artists have completed throughout the years: a bowl of fruit placed on a table.

102 GAUDI

Research online the drawings of Antoni Gaudí and draw your own building inspired by this style.

103   A RURAL OR URBAN LANDSCAPE

Create a drawing of an exterior scene, rural or urban, which you can repeat over the next three days. Firstly, depict the scene as it appears in the current season.

104   A NEW SEASON

Draw the same scene as yesterday but imagine how it changes with the onset of the following season.

105 CHANGING SEASONS

Continuing on from yesterday's exercise, draw your scene in the next season.

106 WINTER, SPRING, SUMMER, AND FALL

Finally, draw your scene in the last of the four seasons, completing this series of season studies.

INTENSIVE WEEK

Get your sketchpad and prepare to draw five larger pieces.

107　**EDGAR DEGAS**: Degas' drawings were most often studies for larger works in oil or pastel. Degas drew many studies of ballet dancers in various situations; while dancing, taking a dance class, or preparing for dance (putting on ballet slippers). His studies captured fleeting moments or dramatic poses. Taking inspiration from Degas, draw a dancer; whether they be a ballet, tap, or break-dancer.

108　**FIGURE STUDIES**: Degas created figure studies using loose, gestural marks with selected areas of finer detail. His subjects were often dancers, musicians, or women bathing; their faces obscured by towels as they dry their hair. Find and copy a Degas figure study.

109　**HORSES**: Another regular subject for Degas was horses and jockeys. He would mostly paint them in the moments prior to a race. His drawings tended to be studies of the horse in motion, with or without the jockey, capturing movements, dimensions, and muscle definition. Sketch a horse, with or without a rider, studying the sinews and contours of its muscles in movement.

110　**MODERN LIFE**: A common theme in the works of Degas was the depiction of modern life; often weary, weathered figures, such as those in *L'Absinthe* (1876). Draw some similarly raw depictions of modern life.

111　**PHOTOGRAPHY**: During the early years of photography, Degas made numerous photographic lamp-lit figure studies. Take photographs of someone lit only by a lamp and make sketches from the images.

"The first sight of Degas' pictures was the turning point of my artistic life."
—Mary Cassatt

112   HEIRLOOM

Draw a family heirloom; something which holds a great deal of sentimental value.

113   INSECT

Draw an insect in motion, such as a spider spinning a web or a bee extracting nectar from a flower.

SUNRISE AND SUNSET

Draw a rural or urban landscape at both sunrise and sunset.

Sunrise

Sunset

DISTORTED PERSPECTIVE

Choosing a room in your home, sketch an abstract, loose drawing, using distorted perspective to give interesting and unexpected results. You could, for example, draw the scene from above so your bed or dining table and chairs appear as flattened shapes.

116 SHEEP

Sketch a solitary sheep or a flock of sheep within a landscape.

117 A NEW FLAG

Design a made-up flag for a country of the world. You could use either a flat graphic style or a more realistic drawing style.

SOLITARY TREE

Draw a solitary tree.

"There are days when I'm completely depressed and able to do only one drawing."

—Christian Lacroix

VANISHING POINT: TREES

Imagine you are standing in the middle of a forest, or among trees in the park, and looking directly up at the treetops. Draw the surrounding trees so that they reach a vanishing point directly above you (this will be near the middle of the page). If you are able, draw this scene from real life.

DRAWING THE SENSES

Interpret in a small sketch the sentence below, from the book *As I Lay Dying* by William Faulkner. Your drawing could be either realistic or abstract.

"Warmish-cool, with a faint taste like the hot July wind in cedar trees smells."

INTENSIVE WEEK

Get your sketchpad and prepare to draw five larger pieces.

121

THE WALK: Take your sketchpad and go for a walk through your town or city, or take a bus ride, producing some rough sketches of things you see along the way. You might sketch people (a law enforcement officer, a storekeeper, a passerby), or buildings (stores, monuments, a place of worship). You might sketch cars, animals, benches, parks. Be prolific in your sketching, but here is the twist: every drawing you do during this week you must use one continuous line. This is the only rule; the line can overlap, scribble, zigzag, undulate, spiral, but it should not leave the page. Let the line "go for a walk," moving freely without too much consideration. Think of it as a stream of consciousness.

122

PEOPLE: Look through one of the sketches from yesterday's walk, choose one of a person and create from this a larger, more detailed drawing. Again, as you draw do not lift your pencil from the paper.

123

ANIMALS OR AUTOMOBILES: Choose a sketch of an animal and create from this a larger, detailed drawing. If you didn't sketch an animal on your walk, choose an automobile instead.

124

LANDMARK: Choose a sketch from your walk of a building or landmark and make a detailed study.

125

MAP: Draw a map of your city and use it to plot your journey from the beginning of this week, using one continuous line. You may wish to sketch in memorable landmarks that you passed along the way.

"A drawing is simply a line going for a walk."
—Paul Klee

126   EMPTY BOTTLE

Draw an empty bottle of beer or soda lying on the table or floor.

127   CRUSHED CAN

Draw a crushed can of beer or soda lying on the table or floor.

128 FAMILY PHOTOGRAPH

Do a rough sketch of a photograph from your own or your family collection, either from memory or from a copy placed in front of you.

129 HISTORICAL PHOTOGRAPH

Do a rough sketch of a famous historical photograph, either from memory or from a copy placed in front of you.

MUSICAL INSPIRATION

Create a drawing inspired by an evocative piece of music, such as "Nimrod" by Elgar, "The Lark Ascending" by Vaughan Williams, "Mars" by Holst, or Beethoven's "Symphony. No. 7."

131 EYES

Using a mirror as a visual aid, draw one or both of your eyes, including your eyebrows. When looking back and forth into a mirror for reference it is important to maintain a consistent body position in order to perfectly capture the image.

132 EAR

Draw one of your ears, building areas of darker tone and negative space in order to create the depth and contours of the ear.

133 NOSE

Draw your nose, considering it in context with the rest of your face, rather than in isolation; i.e., where the contours of your nose meet your cheeks, and how shadows from the bone structure around your eyes affect the appearance of your nose.

134 MOUTH

Draw your mouth. Try to capture a specific emotion, like anger or pensiveness. Subtle considerations, such as the tightness of pursed lips or creases at the corner of the mouth, will affect the mood portrayed.

INTENSIVE WEEK

Get your sketchpad and prepare to draw five larger pieces.

135 **A MUSICIAN:** Draw a musician playing an instrument. If you know any musicians, you could ask them to pose playing for you as you do quick sketches. You could take your pad to a musical event, ask a busker if they would mind you drawing them as they play, or source an image. If you source an image then perhaps you could listen to some music as you draw. You want the feeling of the music to feed into your drawing and inspire your work.

136 **A MUSICAL INSTRUMENT:** Draw a musical instrument propped up, laid down, or in its case.

137 **CLOSE UP:** Draw in close-up detail a section of a musical instrument. This might be the tuning pegs of a guitar, the mouthpiece of a trumpet, or the cymbal of a drum kit, showing the distorted reflections of its surroundings.

138 **AN AUDIENCE:** Sketch an audience at a concert, such as a rock show or piano concerto. You could source an image, draw from memory, or use your imagination; or if you are attending a concert today, take along your pad.

139 **OPPOSITES:** Draw a musician who is the complete opposite of your subject from day 135. If before you drew a jazz saxophonist in a suit, then today choose a heavy metal guitarist in a leather jacket. If before you had a musician pose for you, and they are willing to do so again, draw them today from a completely different angle.

"Drawing is putting a line round an idea."
—Henry Matisse

A MURMURATION OF STARLINGS

Draw a large murmuration of starlings, producing a congregated rise and fall motion in the sky, above a building, trees, or telephone wires. To capture this visual spectacle you could draw a very faint outline of the shape of the flock; a snapshot of their rise and fall. Inside this shape create a tight grid of equally faint lines, following the form of the shape. At each point where the lines meet, pencil in a rough dark representation of a bird. This will help create the impression of the rise and fall of the flock.

141 BIRDS ON THE WIRE

Sketch two or three of yesterday's birds, who have flown away from the flock and have perched on a telephone wire.

SOLITARY BIRD

Draw in detail one of yesterday's birds on its own, either perched or in mid-flight. You may want to source an image to help with the detail.

143   A BIRD'S-EYE VIEW

Draw what the world might look like from the perspective of your bird from yesterday

144 ROCK

Draw a rock, considering the effects of the light source on the angles and undulations of the rock's surface.

145 SEASHELL

Draw a seashell. The swirling pattern of a shell is a golden ratio in nature, with an intrinsic beauty. Capturing the curves and shadows can be a rewarding challenge, but intriguingly any inaccuracies in the golden ratio can have visually jarring effects.

INSPIRATION FROM THE 60s

Taking inspiration from the 1960s, capture a moment, an object, or a sense of the decade.

147   A STEAMING HOT COFFEE

Sketch a cup of coffee, relatively small, in the lower part of the
space below, and fill the rest of the space with the undulating
cloud of steam flowing up from the piping-hot contents of the cup.

148   REPEATING PATTERN

Look for a repeating pattern somewhere in your home, whether it
be the lining inside a coat, a strip of wallpaper, or tiles on the floor.
Using the space below, draw the pattern.

INTENSIVE WEEK

Get your sketchpad and prepare to draw five larger pieces.

149 **BROKEN:** Draw an item that is broken, cracked, burned, or ripped.

150 **UNUSUAL PERSPECTIVE:** Draw part of a building, inside or out, from an unusual perspective, such as looking up through the center of a hotel stairwell.

151 **SCATTERED PHOTOGRAPHS:** Sketch a representation of lots of black-and-white photographs scattered around on a table, the floor, or in an old box. Try to give an impression of some of the figures and places within the photographs.

152 **SMOKING:** Draw a person, or people, smoking. You may want to add a context, or just focus solely on the figure(s). What effect does the smoking of the cigarette, cigar, or pipe have on the body language of the subject, and how can this best be conveyed in the strokes of the pencil?

153 **LIGHTING ANGLES:** Find an object which has a lot of intricate detail. Place it on a table and shine a lamp upon it. Move the lamp and/or object around until you settle upon a position which offers an interesting array of light and shadow, emphasizing the intricate elements of the object. Once you are happy with the composition, draw the object.

"Shadow is a color as light is, but less brilliant; light and shadow are only the relation of two tones."
—Paul Cezanne

154 A SUMMER LEAF

Draw a summer leaf; fresh and vibrant.

155 A LEAF IN FALL

Draw a leaf in fall; wilting and crisp.

INSTRUCTION MANUAL

Imagine you are designing a set of visual diagrams for an instruction manual on how to wrap a birthday present. Draw your step-by-step diagrams in the space below.

157 ROCK CONCERT

In the foreground draw a close-up of a microphone that has been dropped to the floor by the lead singer during a rock concert. In the background draw the faded and obscured packed crowd. Consider the effects of perspective upon the stage floor and the figures in the crowd.

158 STATIONERY

Draw an item of functional stationery, such as a hole punch or stapler, either from a distance or a detailed close-up of a specific section of the item.

159 WHAT DOES IT LOOK LIKE?

Draw three thumbnail sketches of unusual things that are
unfamiliar to you. Avoid sourcing an image and see what your
instincts produce. For example, what does a thistle actually look
like? Or a ukulele?

160 GREATER DETAIL 1

Take one of yesterday's thumbnail sketches, source an image of it,
and draw it in greater detail.

161

GREATER DETAIL 2

Choose another of the thumbnail sketches from day 159, source an image of it, and draw it in greater detail.

162

GREATER DETAIL 3

Source an image of your final thumbnail sketch from day 159, and draw it in greater detail.

INTENSIVE WEEK

Get your sketchpad and prepare to draw five larger pieces.

163   **MESS:** Find somewhere that is messy. Either in your home, your place of work, or if you are an extremely tidy person, look for somewhere farther afield. Mess, such as scattered papers and books laying open, roughly strewn clothing, or overflowing refuse, creates interesting shapes, tones, and textures. Using loose and chaotic marks, draw what mess you see in front of you.

164   **A NEW VIEWPOINT:** Source an image of a famous painting that features people, but not a portrait, such as *American Gothic* (1930) by Grant Wood or *Peasant Wedding* (1568) by Pieter Bruegel. Choose one of the people and draw the scene that they would be seeing in front of them (i.e., the same scene as the artist but from a different perspective). You may want to remain stylistically close to the original painting, or use your own unique stylistic interpretation.

165   **A CITY LANDMARK:** Draw a famous city landmark that has an interesting and unusual structure, such as the Eiffel Tower in Paris, with its interwoven wrought iron beams like lattice pastry.

166   **TIME CAPSULE, 1704:** A time capsule has been found following the demolition of a shopping mall. It is discovered that it was buried in 1704. Draw the scene of its uncovering, the contents of the capsule, or the scene of its original burial.

167   **DREAM VISIT:** Draw a place you've always dreamed of visiting and how you imagine it to look.

> "Drawing is the basis of art. A bad painter cannot draw. But one who draws well can always paint."
>
> —Arshile Gorky

OPPOSITE HAND

Place a few random objects on a table in front of you to create an arrangement for a still life, and then draw using your opposite hand (i.e., if you are right-handed use your left hand). Self-imposed constraints can lead to previously undiscovered ideas, techniques, and approaches. Drawing with the opposite hand may well slow you down, your mind and hand no longer fully in sync, which might lead to unexpected and intriguing results.

AN ICONIC POSE

Sketch a famous historical, political, or sporting figure in an iconic pose, such as Elizabeth Eckford wearing sunglasses, proudly and defiantly carrying her school books into Little Rock Central High School, Arkansas, in 1957, surrounded by military and a baying crowd.

HISTORICAL JUXTAPOSITION

Sketch someone who may have lived in the same era as your iconic figure from yesterday. Draw them in an everyday situation which might serve to juxtapose with yesterday's image; for example, you might draw a young and innocent child playing with a toy.

171 CHAIR

Draw a chair. Is it just a plain, inanimate object or does it seem to have its own character?

172 HANDCRAFTED

Find and draw something which has been handcrafted, capturing any unique qualities and wonderful imperfections.

PAVING SLABS

Draw paving slabs on a sidewalk, a cobbled street, or similar. Many subjects that at first seem somewhat underwhelming can be brought to life with careful observation and become quite enlightening and beautiful. Focus on capturing small details, such as hairline cracks, raised edges that catch the light, the raw beauty of grit and dirt, remnants of aging chewing gum, and anything else you observe.

"A rock pile ceases to be a rock pile the moment a single man contemplates it, bearing within him the image of a cathedral."

—Antoine de Saint-Exupery

UPSIDE DOWN

Interpret in a small sketch (realistic or abstract) the following line from the book *Colorless Tsukuru Tazaki and His Years of Pilgrimage* by Haruki Murakami:

"'The world isn't that easily turned upside down,' Haida replied. 'It's people who are turned upside down.'"

175 BANANA

Draw a peeled banana and its skin.

176 UNUSUAL OBJECT

Find the most unusual object that you have available at this
moment, place it in front of you, and draw it.

INTENSIVE WEEK

Get your sketchpad and prepare to draw five larger pieces.

For this intensive week you will be copying the work of great artists from the past and present. At the bottom of this page are some suggestions of great artists whose works you may like to copy. Feel free to choose any work by any artist who inspires you, and whose techniques and style you would like to learn from.

177 **INSIDE:** Source and copy an image of an interior scene, either by using the Internet or visiting a gallery.

178 **ABSTRACT:** Source and copy an image of a piece of abstract art, either by using the Internet or visiting a gallery.

179 **STILL LIFE:** Source and copy an image of a still life, either by using the Internet or visiting a gallery.

180 **OUTSIDE:** Source and copy an image of an outdoor scene, either by using the Internet or visiting a gallery.

181 **MOVEMENT:** Source and copy an image of a piece of work depicting movement, either by using the Internet or visiting a gallery.

Suggested artists: Jean-Michel Basquiat, Caravaggio, Marc Chagall, John Constable, Leonardo da Vinci, Edgar Degas, Lucian Freud, Frida Kahlo, Lee Krasner, Henri Matisse, Michelangelo, Georgia O'Keeffe, Pablo Picasso, Gerhard Richter, Egon Shiele, Cy Twombly, Vincent van Gogh, Andy Warhol.

"Draw, Antonio, draw—draw and don't waste time!"

—Michelangelo

182 FAMOUS CLOTHING

Think of a famous person who is easily identified by an item
of clothing that they wear or have worn; for example: Michael
Jackson's sparkling white glove, Charlie Chaplin's bowler hat,
or Jackie O's sunglasses. Draw this solitary item of clothing.

183 BUTTERFLY

Draw a butterfly. Consider how you might capture its delicate wings,
or the motion as it flutters.

184 MAP OF THE WORLD

Draw a basic map of the world. Fill in all the areas of water and land with varying patterns, shading, or symbols.

185 OVERLAPPING CIRCLES

Draw a series of overlapping circles. Use different techniques to fill in the various shapes created by these converging shapes. These patterns may spark ideas for something else, or simpy create a unique image.

186 KEYS

Draw a bunch of keys, capturing any unique details or shapes.

HUMMINGBIRD

Draw a hummingbird hovering to retrieve nectar from a flower, capturing its wing speed (fifty flaps per second).

188 PALM UP

Draw something small in the palm of your hand, such as a coin or a piece of candy.

189 REVOLVER

Draw an antique revolver, either from a sourced image or from memory.

INTENSIVE WEEK

Get your sketchpad and prepare to draw five larger pieces.

190   **SPORTING MOVEMENTS:** Sketch a golfer performing a full backswing. The body position will move only slightly, if at all, but the arms, golf club, and shoulders will move in a rhythmic semicircle. Draw the golfer's body, then sketch a few snapshots of the arms, club, and shoulders as they move through the backswing, capturing a dynamic visual of the whole movement.

191   **VARYING VIEWPOINTS:** Using a loose drawing style, produce a study of an animal, showing three varying viewpoints of the same animal on the same page.

192   **HAND STUDY:** Using one piece of paper, draw three studies of your hand in a clenched fist. Each study should be from a different angle.

193   **DRAWING FROM LITERATURE:** Use one or all of the following book titles as inspiration for a drawing:
- *Fear and Loathing in Las Vegas* by Hunter S. Thompson
- *A Tale of Two Cities* by Charles Dickens
- *Where the Wild Things Are* by Maurice Sendak

194   **DUMP TRUCK:** Draw a dump truck. Raw beauty can be found in unexpected places.

> "I do not know if you bridle your pen, but when my pencil moves, it is necessary to let it go, or—crash!... nothing more."
> —Henri de Toulouse-Lautrec

195 BRIDGE

Draw a bridge, either from life or from a sourced image.

196 COIN PURSE OR WALLET

Draw a coin purse or wallet, open or closed, with the contents either intact or spilling out.

THE KISS

Draw your own interpretation of the title given to the famous painting by Gustav Klimt, *The Kiss* (1907–08).

198 METALS

Draw something made of copper, aluminum, silver, or gold.

199 INSPIRATION FROM THE 70s

Draw something from the decade that brought us disco, chopper bikes, and flares.

200 PALM DOWN

Sketch your writing hand, palm down, using your opposite hand.

MEMORY GAME

Observe the palm of your hand for two minutes, then draw it from memory.

CARTOON ANIMAL

Draw a cartoon animal. Whichever animal you choose, draw them standing on two legs in the tradition of characters like Mickey Mouse™ and Bugs Bunny™.

203 SOFA

A sofa is often a well-worn fixture in a home and can seemingly have a character all of its own. Draw your own couch, capturing the finer details, such as any scratches, stains, and indents that will bring it to life on the page.

204 A FOUNTAIN

Draw a fountain. In order to capture the effect of flowing water, consider the way in which light shines on the droplets, and how these droplets dissipate as they reach the end of their cascade.

INTENSIVE WEEK

Get your sketchpad and prepare to draw five larger pieces.

205

THE PENCIL STORY: In 1972–73 John Baldessari created a piece of artwork entitled *The Pencil Story*. The artwork contained two photographs of the same pencil: one blunt, one sharpened. Underneath them he wrote, "I had this old pencil on the dashboard of my car for a long time. Every time I saw it, I felt uncomfortable since its point was so dull and dirty. I always intended to sharpen it and finally couldn't bear it any longer and did sharpen it. I'm not sure, but I think that this has something to do with art." Taking inspiration from the story of Baldessari's pencil (from a car dashboard, sharpened, photographed, and made into a piece of art), take a pencil on a journey. Begin by drawing a blunt pencil in an unexpected place, such as on the dashboard of a car.

206

TIP: Draw a large close-up picture showing the tip of the blunt pencil.

207

SHAVINGS: Sharpen the pencil and draw a close-up of the shavings.

208

WIDER COMPOSITION: Draw the newly sharpened pencil in a different location, for example on a table or windowsill.

209

SOMETHING TO DO WITH ART: Swapping between the now sharp pencil and the one you have been using to draw, using one to draw the other, sketch the two pencils side by side. Underneath this, write a few sentences to describe your own "Pencil Story" from the past week, perhaps ending with Baldessari's line "I'm not sure, but I think that this has something to do with art."

> "Look at the subject as if you have never seen it before. Examine it from every side. Draw its outline with your eyes or in the air with your hands, and saturate yourself with it."
>
> —John Baldessari

210 CAT

Draw a cat. This might be a quick sketch from life, capturing the cat in a fleeting moment, or a more detailed drawing from a sourced image.

211 GORILLA

Draw a gorilla. Use either a photo-realistic style or create a cartoon character.

A SINGLE BRANCH

Draw a single branch of a tree, perhaps with foliage growing from it.

213 | HAMBURGER

Draw a hamburger in its opened box or wrapper. In the background sketch the setting, such as the fast-food restaurant where the hamburger was purchased.

214 | PLAYING CARDS

Draw a deck of cards or a single playing card. You might want to create a detailed study of a single card, or perhaps a more playful, loose drawing of the pack spewed across a table.

215   POP ART

Using the unique style of pop art, draw a note or coin of currency, such as a one-dollar bill. For inspiration, you may want to explore the styles of artists such as Andy Warhol, Roy Lichtenstein, and Jasper Johns.

216   POINTILLISM

Pointillism is a technique that uses tiny dots or "points" from a pencil to create an image. The technique was used to great affect by artists, such as Paul Signac and Georges Seurat. Using this technique, draw a note or coin of currency.

217 CUBISM

Cubism is an art movement, pioneered by Georges Braque and Pablo Picasso, who broke up their images into abstract forms and often captured their subjects from multiple viewpoints at once. Using a cubist style, draw a note or coin of currency.

218 SURREALISM

Surrealism created dreamlike imagery and distorted reality. Draw a note or coin of currency using this style, perhaps melting like the clocks in *The Persistence of Memory* (1931) by Salvador Dalí.

INTENSIVE WEEK

Get your sketchpad and prepare to draw five larger pieces.

219

DRAWING EN PLEIN AIR: There is a great tradition of artists going out into the open air and painting or drawing *in situ*. Inspiration is everywhere: rusted old ships in a dockyard, sculptures in a park, fountains, fences, graveyards, or lakes. Take your pencil and pad outside to a local environment, look for inspiration, and draw. For example, if you live near an industrial estate then find a safe place from where you can observe and draw. There might be piles of wood and metal beams, cargo containers, cranes, and workers.

220

BOOKSHELF: Sketch a bookshelf or row upon row of books in a library.

221

NATURAL PHENOMENON: Draw a natural or extreme weather phenomenon, such as lava flow, a geyser in a national park, a tornado, a tidal wave, or the aftereffects of an earthquake.

222

GRAFFITI: Draw a scene filled with interesting graffiti, either from life or a sourced image.

223

LITERARY CHARACTER: Draw a famous character from literature, such as Jane Eyre, Jay Gatsby, or Huckleberry Finn.

"You can't do sketches enough. Sketch everything and keep your curiosity fresh."
—John Singer Sargent

224 POLITICAL SATIRE

Draw a caricature of a famous politician, either current or historical.

225 UNEXPECTED COMPARISONS

Draw two objects side by side that are completely different but have something in common, such as their texture, shape, or sentimental value to you.

226

SHADOW BOXER

Draw the wall shadow of a shadow boxer.

227 SILENCE

How might you interpret "silence" in a small sketch?

228 CAMEL

Draw a camel from a sourced image, sketching in a background to provide a context.

ORIGAMI BIRD

Find an image of a bird and draw a basic outline of it. Use geometric shapes, such as triangles and parallelograms, to build up the body of the image within this outline (see the example below). These shapes will mimic the shapes created by origami paper folds. Once the shape of the bird is fully formed, shade in each of the geometric shapes to give the appearance of folded paper.

THE SNAIL

Draw your own interpretation of the title given to the famous collage by Henri Matisse, *The Snail* (1953).

"The visionary starts with a clean sheet of paper, and re-imagines the world."
—Malcolm Gladwell

DRAWING WITH WRITING

Choose a passage from a well-known novel or your favorite book. Draw a basic outline of an image that represents the content of this writing, and fill in this outline using only the words from your chosen passage. You could add shading by using heavy pencil marks for some of the words.

232   SCHOOL BUS

Draw a school bus. Use a sourced image to draw a stationary bus, or sit in a place where you can watch traffic and draw the buses as they go by. If doing the latter, then draw in stages, capturing different elements of each bus that passes with fast, fleeting movements of the pencil until you have a complete image.

233   A PIER

Draw a pier, either from a sourced image or from life.

INTENSIVE WEEK

Get your sketchpad and prepare to draw five larger pieces.

234   **THE DAWN CHORUS**: Draw a representation of the dawn chorus; the time when the sun rises and birds sing together to pronounce the start of the day. Whether your work is a true-to-life representation of the birds and their environment, or an abstract, conceptual response, try to convey the sense of song and the dawning of the day.

235   **OLD AND DECAYING:** Sketch a deteriorating wall. Look for a wall that is as run-down as possible, with worn bricks, graffiti, flaking paint, or areas of dampness.

236   **SKULL:** Skulls are a common motif seen throughout the history of art, from *Portrait of a Young Man with a Skull* (1662–68) by Frans Hals to Damien Hirst's *For the Love of God* (2006). Draw a human skull.

237   **CLAIMED BY WATER:** Draw an image of Venice, Italy, (densely populated and built on 118 islands with a network of rising-level waterways) in an imaginary apocalyptic future where the city has become almost completely claimed by water. Alternatively, choose another city to draw in an apocalyptic watery future.

238   **MOVIE POSTER:** Draw your own movie poster for a film of your choosing.

"You can never do too much drawing."
—Jacopo Tintoretto

239 FLOWERS

Draw an array of flowers in a flower shop, park, or garden.

240 CURTAINS

Sketch a pair of curtains. Inanimate objects can sometimes evoke emotion and drama. Curtains can certainly do this, with their textures, folds, drapes, areas of light and dark, and the flowing movement created by a breeze from an open window.

JUMPING IN THE AIR

Draw a person jumping in the air. What is the effect of this movement on the different parts of their body, such as their arms, legs, and feet? How might you best capture their hair as it floats up and down?

242 DINOSAUR

Draw a dinosaur, either from an image, your imagination, or a toy.

243 A DOG

Draw a dog, using a series of very thin marks with your pencil to capture the detail of the dog's hair.

CLASSICAL SCULPTURE

Sketch a famous classical sculpture, such as Michelangelo's *David*.

245 SCISSORS

Draw a pair of scissors, either the whole object or a close-up of a section.

246 HAUNTED HOUSE

Draw a haunted house. What effects can you use to get across the idea that it is haunted?

INTENSIVE WEEK

Get your sketchpad and prepare to draw five larger pieces.

247

ART INFORMEL: Art Informel was an abstract art movement in the 1940s and 50s. Its central approach was improvisation and gestural techniques. The artist would begin with their materials and no prior expectation of the finished work. They would let the instinctive feel of the brush, charcoal, pencil, or whatever medium they were using, guide their mark-making. Using a soft pencil, such as a 6B, make an initial mark on your paper, and then let the feel of the pencil on paper guide how you proceed. Have no expectations of subject or form, just tap into the feel of the lead transferring to paper.

248

MODERN SCULPTURE: Sketch a piece of modern sculpture; for example, *Bird in Space* (1923) by Constantin Brâncuşi. You could either draw from an image or, if possible, go to an art gallery and draw from there. In what ways do the forms differ from classical sculpture?

249

TATTOO: Draw a body part that has an elaborate tattoo. Choose something that has interesting contours, such as an arm, a leg, or a hand. These contours create distortions in the appearance of the tattoo. It is a fun challenge to capture accurately any lettering or intricate artwork.

250

SANDY PLACES: Draw a beach, desert island, or sand dune.

251

CHESS PIECE: Draw two chess pieces side by side; one white, one black. How does the light source affect the tones of each of the chess pieces?

"Drawing is rather like playing chess: your mind races ahead of the moves that you eventually make."

—David Hockney

252 CANDY BAR

Draw a candy bar, wrapped or unwrapped (perhaps half eaten).

253 CELL PHONE

Draw a person using a cell phone.

OUTSIDE THE WINDOW

Look outside your window or, if you are outside, look at what is around you. Use the grid below to draw what you see, paying close attention to the detail. The grid can help you with the composition and scale of your drawing.

A DETAILED VIEW

Choose a section from yesterday's drawing. Use the grid below to draw this section in greater detail.

FLOWING HAIR

Draw somebody with long and flowing hair.

257   EVERYDAY THINGS

Draw a thumbnail sketch of each of the following everyday things, without using any reference:

- shopping cart
- vacuum cleaner
- toaster

258   FLYING THE FLAG

Draw a flag flapping in the wind, aiming to achieve the sense of movement.

WATERFALL

Draw a waterfall. You may want to use an eraser to pick out any flecks of light reflecting off the cascading water.

MAJESTIC BIRDS

Draw an eagle, condor, or vulture.

INTENSIVE WEEK

Get your sketchpad and prepare to draw five larger pieces.

261 **A NIGHT AT THE OPERA:** Sketch a scene from an opera house, capturing the atmosphere of the performers, musicians, and the audience. Try to match the fluidity of motion and sound with that of your pencil, making loose, gestural marks on the page.

262 **FIRST SENTENCE:** Open a book at random and create a drawing inspired by the first sentence you read.

263 **ROOFTOP SILHOUETTE:** Draw a silhouette of rooftops and trees and/or telephone wires in the fading light. Silhouettes against a fading sky create a wonderful contrast of tones. Branches of trees and wiring can create a fantastic pattern against the sky.

264 **SIDE-ON SELF-PORTRAIT:** Draw a portrait of your face as seen from the side, so that you can only see one of your ears.

265 **SCHOOL SUBJECTS:** Think of a subject you studied at school and try to represent it in an image.

"I paint self-portraits because I am so often alone, because I am the person I know best."

—Frida Kahlo

266 AGING APPLIANCES

Draw an electrical appliance, such as a teakettle, toaster, or iron, paying close attention to all those elements which come with age; for example: scorch marks on the iron, scratches on the teakettle, or rust on the toaster.

267 SALTWATER FISH

Draw a saltwater fish swimming in the sea, either from a sourced image or from your imagination.

CITYSCAPE

Draw a cityscape from high up, whether it be from a very tall tower, a skyscraper, or a hillside on the outskirts of a city.

269   SNOW SPORTS 1

Draw somebody skiing, including an impression of the mountain scenery in the background.

270   SNOW SPORTS 2

Draw somebody snowboarding, perhaps performing a trick, and include a setting for your image.

271 MOONLIT NIGHT

Draw a scene that is lit by moonlight.

272 FIREWORKS

Draw fireworks exploding in the sky.

273 STORMY SKY

Draw a stormy night, either from your imagination, or if the wind is up where you are today, draw from reality.

274 *THE STARRY NIGHT*

Copy or draw your own interpretation of Vincent van Gogh's *The Starry Night* (1889).

INTENSIVE WEEK

Get your sketchpad and prepare to draw five larger pieces.

275   **FERRIS WHEEL:** Draw a ferris wheel at a fairground, from memory, from a sourced image, or from life.

276   **FRESH FALL LEAVES:** Create a drawing which represents the action and feeling of walking on fresh fall leaves.

277   **DISTORTED PERSPECTIVE:** Ask somebody to sit for you, take a quick photograph of someone, or use your imagination to draw a figure sitting down with their legs crossed and their arms resting on their knees. Experiment with different viewpoints: for example, you could sit on the floor and have your subject pose on a chair or table in front of you. Capturing this distorted perspective is challenging but highly rewarding.

278   **REVISIT AND REIMAGINE:** Revisit one of your drawings in this book that you feel you would like to develop further. Perhaps you produced a thumbnail or sketch that you would like to draw in more detail, or on a larger scale. By flicking through your drawings you may find inspiration for a new subject, or reimagine an existing one.

279   **LAUGHTER:** Draw something that makes you laugh.

"I cannot rest, I must draw, however poor the result, and when I have a bad time come over me it is a stronger desire than ever."

—Beatrix Potter

280 SCRATCHES

Find an object which has very subtle scratches on it, such as an antique gold ring, a saucepan, or a paperweight. Try to bring the subtle scratches to the page by using delicate pencil strokes.

281 EVERGREEN FOREST

Draw the edge of an evergreen forest far away on the horizon. Use your imagination to complete the foreground.

IMAGE PROGRESSION 1

Draw a series of four small thumbnail sketches, starting with a hot-air balloon. With each thumbnail that follows draw something that relates to the previous image. For example, you might associate a hot-air balloon with a cloud, then a cloud with rain, and so on.

IMAGE PROGRESSION 2

Take your final drawing from yesterday's image progression exercise and draw it again in greater detail.

284 BREAK-DANCE

Draw a break-dancer in motion. Try using your non-dominant hand to complete this drawing. Constraints like this can add a raw quality to your work, reflecting the style of your subject.

285 BALLROOM

Using one continuous line, sketch a pair of ballroom dancers, allowing the flow of the pencil to mirror their flowing movements.

OLD-FASHIONED CAR

Without taking your pencil from the page, draw an old-fashioned car. You may want to play around with the angle the car is viewed from in order to fit it in the space below; for example, with the car hood in the foreground and the back of the car farther into the distance.

"To draw, you must close your eyes and sing."

—Pablo Picasso

287 ORNATE

Draw something ornate, like a baroque picture frame, intricate cabinetry, or the edge of an old lace tablecloth.

COLORING BOOK

Draw an outline of an image which might be used for a coloring book. Choose something as simple or as elaborate as you like, but ensure the final outlines are very clear and deliberate. This may be a technique you enjoy using within your drawing, and can also be used for structuring a watercolor painting or ink drawing.

INTENSIVE WEEK

Get your sketchpad and prepare to draw five larger pieces.

289 **DIFFERENT PERSPECTIVES:** Using a loose drawing style, produce a study of a friend or relative, from life or from a photo, showing three different perspectives of the same person on the same page.

290 **NOSTALGIA:** Create a drawing in response to the idea of "nostalgia," whatever that word means to you.

291 **NBA LOGOS:** Choose an NBA basketball team logo and create a realistic representation of the logo's icon. For example, draw a raging bull for the Chicago Bulls, or for the New York Knicks draw a 17th-Century Dutch Settler to America, complete with knee-high "knickerbocker" trousers.

292 **RICKSHAW:** Draw a form of transport you wouldn't normally expect to see, such as a rickshaw or a horse and cart.

293 **ART DECO:** Search online for "Art Deco architecture" and draw your own building in this style.

"Drawing is an immediate way of articulating [an] idea—of making a gesture that is both physical and intellectual."

—Jeff Koons

294 WOOD GRAIN

Draw a close-up study of a piece of wood, or something made from wood that has a very distinct grain.

295 GEOMETRIC PATTERN

Draw a faint outline of a simple object found in your home. Fill the shape you have created with a series of interconnecting diamonds and triangles, then use different tones to shade these in, creating a dynamic image.

296 SAILBOAT

Use a sourced image or your memory to draw a sailboat, or if you live near the sea, use a real-life reference.

297 *TROMPE L'ŒIL*

Draw a *trompe l'œil* (a trick of the eye). Create the illusion that the space on this page has been ripped apart, revealing something underneath. Aim to make the effect of the torn paper as realistic as possible.

INSPIRATION FROM THE 80s

Try to find an object from the 1980s in your home, such as a cassette player or early games console, and draw it. If you don't have anything in your home, find an image online or from a book.

299 DRAWING CONSTRAINTS: CURVES

Applying self-imposed drawing constraints can be excellent for creativity, forcing us to think differently and generating unexpected, potentially inspiring results. Draw a rural landscape using only curved lines.

300 DRAWING CONSTRAINTS: STRAIGHT LINES

Set up a still life on a table and draw it using only straight lines.

301 DRAWING CONSTRAINTS: SHADING

Draw three basic outlines of a row of trees or buildings. Fill in each shape using just one method of shading; for example: hatch, crosshatch, blending, or dots.

302 DRAWING CONSTRAINTS: PATTERNS

If you drew outlines of trees yesterday then draw outlines of buildings today, or the other way around. Fill in each shape using a single geometric pattern.

INTENSIVE WEEK

Get your sketchpad and prepare to draw five larger pieces.

303

ANIMAL PAINTING: Source an image of a famous painting that features animals. Choose one of the animals and draw the scene that the animal would be seeing in front of them (i.e., draw the same scene as the artist but from a different perspective). You may want to remain stylistically close to the original painting, or use your own stylistic interpretation.

304

VITRIOL: Draw a picture of somebody shouting angrily with mouth wide open. How might you convey the sense of anger and vitriol in your drawing? The lines of the face and neck, when strong emotions are let out, can show strain and tension. By tapping into the feelings of the subject you can also channel that emotion into your work, helping to inform the strokes of your pencil.

305

ANGLED SELF-PORTRAIT: Using a portable mirror draw a self-portrait from a low-level angle, looking up at your neck and face.

306

WILD ANIMALS: Draw a wild animal, such as a wolf, bear, or boar. This might be a study, perhaps involving various sketches of the animal from different angles, or a detailed depiction of the animal in its natural environment.

307

JUNKYARD: Draw a junkyard, or a similar environment, from life, your imagination, or a sourced image. You'll find that the various objects around provide a lot of interesting textures, dark shadows, and areas of light.

"I had great masters. I took the best of … their examples. I found myself, I made myself, and I said what I had to say."

—Suzanne Valadon

308 *THE SCREAM*

Draw your own interpretation of the title given to the famous painting by Edvard Munch, *The Scream* (1893).

AN ICONIC POSE

Sketch a famous historical, political, or sporting figure in an iconic pose, such as Martin Luther King Jr. on the podium outside the Lincoln Memorial in 1963, delivering his "I Have a Dream" speech.

HISTORICAL JUXTAPOSITION

Draw something which might serve to contrast with your image from yesterday; for example, you might draw a person wearing dirty clothes and standing in a welfare line, portraying a lack of hope.

312 ORANGE

Draw an orange with its skin either fully or partially peeled.

309 PERFECT MEAL

Draw your idea of a perfect meal.

313 A NASTY BITE

Draw a spider or mosquito.

314 A STING IN THE TAIL

Draw a rattlesnake or scorpion.

STORYBOARD

Use the six frames below to create a storyboard, representing an action from a movie, book, your life, or something imagined. Each drawing need only be a loose representation of the action, people, and places.

IN THE FRAME

Choose one of the six frames from yesterday's storyboard and sketch it out in greater detail.

INTENSIVE WEEK

Get your sketchpad and prepare to draw five larger pieces.

317   **MARKETPLACE:** Draw a stand at a farmer's market, from life or from a sourced image, including the produce on sale, such as meats, cheeses, or vegetables.

318   **SUPERMARKET SHELF:** Draw a shelf in a supermarket, from life or from a sourced image, including the various produce on offer.

319   **REACHING:** Draw a figure study of somebody stretching or reaching for something. You might draw from life (having a friend or relative pose for you), or an image of a sports person, such as a tennis player stretching to reach for a ball. The key is to really observe the sinews, muscles, and balance of the subject. It is a challenge to capture the sense of strained movement and balance, and avoid a static, limp figure.

320   **SO APPEALING:** In 1956 the artist Richard Hamilton created a collage with the sardonic title *Just What is it That Makes Today's Homes so Different, So Appealing?* He depicted a fake consumer paradise in a 1950s living room. Take inspiration from Hamilton's work and create your own consumer paradise, filled with scattered tokens of modern-day objects of desire.

321   **DEMOLITION:** Draw a building pre-, post-, or during demolition.

"Let the world burn through you. Throw the prism light, white hot, on paper."
— Ray Bradbury

322 COOKIES

Draw a single cookie or a jar of cookies.

323 OLD AGE

Create a still life in response to the idea of "old age."

ELEPHANT

Draw an elephant. The texture of an elephant's skin offers an interesting challenge because it is very tough, cracked, full of linear and crosshatched creases.

325 · BREAKFAST

Draw something you might find at breakfast time, such as
a box of cereal, or a jar of strawberry jam and a knife.

326 · A TRAIN

Draw a train. You could draw the full length of the train, either
in motion or standing at a station. Alternatively, you could draw a
close-up view, or draw the train moving towards a vanishing point
on the horizon.

AN EXPLOSION OF DRAWINGS

Sketch random examples of things that you love and hate, places you like to go, and things you think about, covering this entire page, like an explosion or wave of drawings.

STAIRWAY

Draw a stairway, considering the effects of perspective on the scale of each step as they ascend or descend in front of you, depending on your viewpoint.

"I prefer drawing to talking. Drawing is faster, and leaves less room for lies."
—Le Corbusier

NATURAL MATERIALS

Draw something made of wool, cotton, or wood.

330 THE FLOWER CARRIER

Draw your own interpretation of the title given to the famous painting by Diego Rivera, *The Flower Carrier* (1935).

331 A SMOKING CIGAR

Use the lower portion of the space below to draw a cigar in an ashtray, and fill the rest of the space with its unfurling smoke.

INTENSIVE WEEK

Get your sketchpad and prepare to draw five larger pieces.

332   **MUSEUM:** Visit a museum, or if you are unable to visit a museum, research museum displays online. Sketch a museum artifact or a full display of them.

333   **CHILDHOOD PLACE:** Sketch from memory a room or place that was important to you as a child. If your memories are hazy then consider how you could represent this in your drawing by, for example, drawing a hazily rendered sketch.

334   **ANCIENT STRUCTURE:** Draw an ancient structure, such as Stonehenge (UK), Machu Picchu (Peru), or if you are lucky enough to have such a site local to you then visit it and sketch away.

335   **BRIGHT LIGHTS, BIG CITY:** Draw a scene with many bright lights and commercial hoardings, such as Times Square in New York, Shibuya Crossing in Tokyo, or the street markets of Hong Kong. To bring detail into every neon sign and commercial banner would be an exhaustive feat. Aim to create an impression of the overall scene, using gestural strokes together with some selected areas of finer detail.

336   **UNUSUAL BUILDING:** Draw what might be considered an unusual building, such as a Japanese pagoda, a tree house, or a lighthouse.

"Don't wait for moods. You accomplish nothing if you do that. Your mind must know it has got to get down to work."
—Pearl S. Buck

337 AT THE GAS STATION

Use your memory or a sourced image to draw a gas pump.

338 A PICTURE IS WORTH A THOUSAND WORDS

Draw a scene from an old photograph, perhaps one that is sentimental to you. You could either work from memory or by observing the photograph in front of you.

MONKEY

Draw a monkey in its natural habitat. This might be a squirrel monkey in the Amazon rain forest or a rhesus macaque living in the Indian city of Jaipur.

340 DROPPED AT THE CARNIVAL

Draw something that might be dropped on the ground at a carnival.

341 EGGSHELL

Draw an egg in its shell, either in an egg cup, on its own, or cracked.

ANATOMY

There is a long tradition of artists studying human anatomy through detailed sketches. Leonardo da Vinci mapped the human body with a series of anatomical studies, culminating in *The Vitruvian Man* (1490). Taking inspiration from these classic human studies, draw a detailed sketch of a part of the human anatomy, or a study of the human physique.

343 VANISHING POINT: PATHWAY

Draw a scene that includes a pathway, river, or road disappearing into a vanishing point.

344 SNEEZE

Using your imagination, or a sourced image, draw a portrait of a person in mid-sneeze.

INTENSIVE WEEK

Get your sketchpad and prepare to draw five larger pieces.

345 **INHERITANCE:** Draw something you have inherited from your parents. This might be an object or one of your facial features.

346 **SPORTS STADIUM:** Sketch an empty or fan-filled sports stadium from inside, outside, or above. Alternatively, sketch an object which might be found inside a sports stadium, such as a hotdog or baseball cap.

347 **BOATS:** Use a sourced image to draw a barge, cruise ship, or fishing trawler. It could be in a dock, junkyard, or out at sea.

348 **ELDERLY PORTRAIT:** Draw a portrait of an elderly person. Wrinkles and broken skin create shadows. It is important to observe these carefully and use a range of tones in your drawing to capture the differentiations in light and shade.

349 **SURREALISM:** In 1938 Salvador Dalí produced a piece of artwork entitled *Lobster Telephone*, a mixed-media sculpture of a telephone with a lobster forming part of the receiver. Taking inspiration from this work, draw your own surreal composition; an amusing arrangement of disparate objects fashioned together into a bizarre and surprising image.

"Surrealism is destructive, but it destroys only what it considers to be shackles limiting our vision."

—Salvador Dalí

350 INSPIRATION FROM THE 90s

Sketch something from the 1990s, whether it be an image, an object, or a memory.

351

FIVE-MINUTE SKETCH: WIND TURBINES

In just five minutes, draw a vista of wind turbines leading to a vanishing point. The sizes of each turbine will vary according to the perspective created by the vanishing point.

352

FIVE-MINUTE SKETCH: TORTOISE

Draw a tortoise in five minutes. Let your pencil fly across the page, making interpretative marks to create the idea and essence of the animal. A likeness is less important than fluidity.

A FAMOUS CARICATURE

Draw a caricature of a well-known celebrity.

354 *SELF-PORTRAIT WITH TWO CIRCLES*

Draw your own interpretation of the title given to the famous painting by Rembrandt, *Self-portrait with Two Circles* (c. 1665–69).

CAMPBELL'S SOUP

Taking inspiration from *Campbell's Soup Cans* (1962) by Andy Warhol, a work which depicts each of the company's 32 varieties of soup, draw a can of food.

SONG INSPIRATION

Use one or all of the following song titles as inspiration for a drawing:

- "The Handwriting on the Wall" (The Dominoes)
- "Picture on the Wall" (Southern Mountain Boys)
- "These Walls of Memories" (Lamar Morris)

357 ENVELOPE

Draw the front of an envelope, new or old, including the stamp and address.

358 CUTLERY

Draw a knife, fork, and spoon.

INTENSIVE WEEK

Get your sketchpad and prepare to draw five larger pieces.

359 **NEAREST OBJECT:** Grab the nearest object to you and draw it in detail, either in its entirety or honing in on a close-up section of it.

360 **TIME CAPSULE, 1984:** A time capsule has been found following the digging up of turf on a school football field. It is discovered that the capsule was buried in 1984. Draw the scene of its uncovering, the contents of the capsule, or the scene of its original burial.

361 **ONE DRAWING:** Look through your work in this book or your sketchpad and choose one drawing to develop further.

362 **BABE RUTH'S PANTS:** Choose a sports star whose character can be represented by an item of clothing which they famously wore; for example, Babe Ruth's magnificent baseball pants, covered in earth and grit. Draw that item of clothing.

363 **CRACKED MIRROR:** Imagine a cracked mirror (avoid breaking one!) and the distorted images it creates. Draw a cracked mirror, then add in the fragmented reflection.

"Who knows when a trenchant line becomes a human face?"

—Ben Shahn

364 DISTANT PLANET

Draw Earth as it would look from the Moon.

365 CELL PHONE PHOTO

Search your cell phone or digital camera for a photo you have taken that would make an interesting drawing.

SKETCHPAD AND IDEAS FOR FUTURE DRAWINGS